MW00901428

Story Tells
A Story About Organizing

Renee Boney-Jett

George and his big sister Linda are going to the barbershop with Dad.

It has been a long time since they could visit.

Linda is excited and George can't keep still.

The barbershop looks a lot different today. The change made George not want to stay.

"Linda, look! The windows are covered!" George says with his eyes real big.

Linda didn't want George to worry. "George, it's alright. I bet the inside will look just right," Linda says and holds his hand. George's eyes don't look so big anymore.

Linda was right. Inside the barbershop things looked the same. George even saw a cool picture frame.

"Look! My name is there on that wall," says George, pointing to the sign that reads, 'Justice for George'.

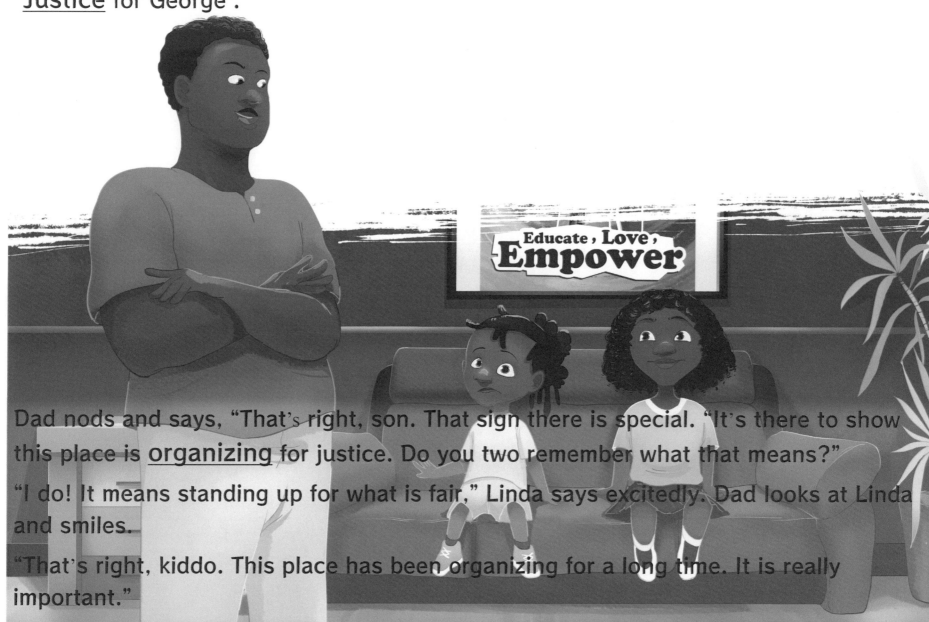

Educate, Love, Empower

Dad nods and says, "That's right, son. That sign there is special. "It's there to show this place is organizing for justice. Do you two remember what that means?"

"I do! It means standing up for what is fair," Linda says excitedly. Dad looks at Linda and smiles.

"That's right, kiddo. This place has been organizing for a long time. It is really important."

George was still confused about the word *organizing.* He looks at Linda and says, "I don't get it, Linda. What does organizing look like?"

All of a sudden someone yells, "Hey, hey, over here! I bet I can explain it crystal clear."

George and Linda look up and see a painting talking to them!

"Wow, the painting is alive!" says Linda with great surprise.

"Hi! My name's Story," the painting says with a smile.

"You're just a painting. What could you know?" George doesn't think Story has anything cool to show them.

Story nods and says, "I may be a painting but I know many spots where people have been organizing around the clock."

"Will you show us, please?" Linda begs. Story smiles at the siblings and nods.

All of a sudden, something magical happens and the walls start to spin. Linda and George know an **adventure** is coming.

"Are we still in a barbershop?" Linda asks quietly.

"Yes, but we traveled back in time, dear. You see 1860 is the year,"
Story whispers.

"But how did they organize?" George asks. "We are so far in the past."

"Not every Black person used to be able to live freely. The people in this barbershop
organized to help Black people escape to <u>freedom discreetly</u>,"
Story says to the siblings.

Story really does know what organizing looks like.

"Let's look at more organizing," Story says, and everything starts spinning again. How exciting!

Linda and George look all around. It looks really cool. "Wow, there's so many people here!" George says with his eyes wide once again.

"Welcome to 1920. In this shop people gave haircuts for free," Story says.

"Is this how they organized?" asks Linda.

"Sure is! Not everyone had money for a trim. So, this shop organized by giving free haircuts to her, him, and him!"

George smiles and Linda says, "I like this very much."

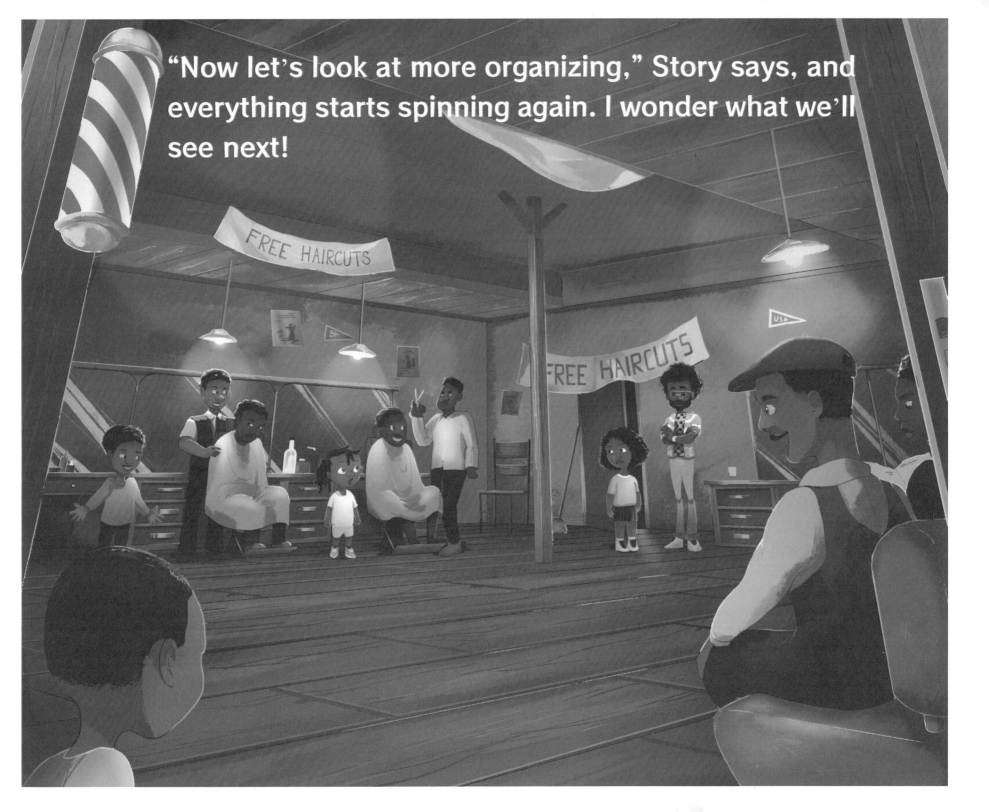

"Now let's look at more organizing," Story says, and everything starts spinning again. I wonder what we'll see next!

"Welcome, my friends, to 1960. Where the city here sure is busy," Story says with a wink.

"How are they organizing here?" asks George.

"The good folks here are all going to <u>march.</u>

In just a moment it all will start," Story says, then gives Linda and George signs.

"We can join too?" the siblings ask with excitement.

"That's right, my friend. We've seen others organize again and again. Now it's our turn to join it all. We'll stand for justice and we'll stand tall. That's what these people are marching for and we can join them with signs <u>galore!</u>" Story shouts.

Standing hand in hand, they're ready to see what organizing really can be.

Walking down the street with their signs held high, Linda says, "I feel proud of my people and loved in this crowd." George nodded.

"Linda dear, I'm so glad you feel proud! Now I want to show you other kids in the crowd," Story says, then pulls out a picture with no color.

Rosemary Freeman, Horace Huntley and Warran Tucker, Minneapolis,
Minnesota. Photo courtesy of University of Minnesota Archives

"These young people know how to organize too.

They stand for justice through and through," says Story.

"Okay, Story, but what about now? Are there kids still marching?
Are we allowed?" asks George.

Photo courtesy of Marika Pfefferkorn, personal collection.

Story pulls out another picture and says,

"This one is new. It has lots of color, and kids like you."

"Kids are still organizing, and they have lots to say. When we go back,

I hope you share what you learned today," Story says.

"We're leaving now?" Linda asks sadly.

"Yes, this adventure is over but don't worry, friend. Your story doesn't end here; it has yet to begin," Story answers. Then everything starts spinning one last time.

The kids have returned to their barbershop. Dad sees them and asks, "Where have you been?"

"Oh Dad, we've been on an adventure! We learned about organizing and saw all kinds of strong people," George says.

"That sounds great, kiddo. How about telling the whole shop what you saw?" Dad says with a smile.

While the siblings are getting their hair done, they explain organizing to EVERYONE.

Linda says proudly, "We saw folks organizing in big and small crowds. Even kids like us can do organizing."

Then George stands up and asks, "Mr. Barber, is there organizing here we can do?"

Mr. Barber nods and says "Oh yes that's something we'd love to see. It's great you are standing up for your community. How about tomorrow we do something fun. We'll give free haircuts for everyone!"

Linda and George were proud to know they had the power to organize.

Linda and George looked at Story. "Thank you, friend, for this most amazing day."

"I can't wait to see what you kids grow up to do. Good luck with organizing, good luck to you." Story says with a farewell wink.

THE END

Glossary

Organizing – To create a group of people with shared goals, mostly to make change.

Justice – The fair treatment of people.

Discreetly – In a careful way; or Carefully.

Freedom – The right to do or say what you want without anyone stopping you.

March – To walk the streets in a group.

Galore – In large amounts; or Alot.

Adventure – A different, exciting experience.[1]

---

[1] *Oxford English Dictionary.* 2nd ed. Oxford: Oxford University Press, 2004.

CPSIA information can be obtained
at www.ICGtesting.com
Printed in the USA
BVRC091309290421
606128BV00011B/457

* 9 7 8 0 5 7 8 8 6 4 6 9 3 *